GRATITUDE
A MINDFUL PAUSE

BY MIRA DESSY, BFA, NE, BCHHP &
KERRY McCLURE BS, RYT, NC, BCHN*

Permission requests, speaking arrangements, and wholesale inquiries may be addressed to
Versadia Press, PO Box 1181 Willis TX 77378
www.VersadiaPress.com

Printed in the United States of America 1st printing – February 2018
ISBN: 978-0-9889357-3-0
Graphic Designer Stacy Coale, Bluehaus Design Co.
Front and Back Cover Photo Credit Kerry McClure

DISCLAIMER

*The authors of this book are not doctors. The information in the book should not be
considered medical advice and is not intended to treat, diagnose, prevent or
cure any conditions, physical or otherwise. If you require medical advice or attention,
please consult a physician or other health professional. Information provided
in this book has not been reviewed or approved by any federal, state, or local agency
or healthcare group. Opinions expressed are solely those of the authors and
do not represent any particular individual or professional group.*

A MOMENT TO PAUSE

For me, there has always been something so interesting and inviting about a bench – intrigued by what it's made out of, wondering about the plaque on the back of the bench that shares a small but unknown story, curious as to why the bench is located where it is, and just the gentle invitation to sit down and pause.

The bench on the cover of our journal is no exception. It's one of my favorite benches. Its location is the Santa Cruz, California coastline. What it's made out of is a beautiful mosaic inlaid glass in cement with no backing or plaque. I often sit there for long periods of time just staring out at the beautiful landscape and feeling so grateful for the moment and experience. I could not help but take a picture of this creatively beautiful bench overlooking the magnificent Pacific Ocean to remind me of those peaceful interludes.

The iconic poster for the movie Forrest Gump depicts Tom Hanks sitting on a park bench, the spot where he re-tells his life story to complete strangers. In Philadelphia there is a series of storytelling benches scattered throughout the city. The bench calls to us to pause, listen, and share a bit of our life story.

No matter the weather, the bench is always there. It knows the hearts of those who sit on the bench as they look out at the view from their seat. The bench reminds us to stop, pause and appreciate each day that we have.

How many times have you passed an empty bench, sat down and pondered the worlds' or your own challenges or struck up a conversation with a total stranger?

The bench invites us to practice being in the moment, to breathe slower, talk slower, respond after careful consideration, ask thoughtful questions, be still, and listen. What a privilege it is to be alive, breathe, think, enjoy, and love.

The bench invites us to be in the moment. That's when you realize what you authentically want and truly need. It's also what your heart truly doesn't want and what your soul doesn't need. It's not always about finding yourself, but creating yourself because you want something different. The power of the pause allows for the space to tap into our authentic selves.

Sometimes the change is by choice, and sometimes it's not. When you try to control everything, you enjoy nothing. Sometimes you just need to sit on a bench, relax, breathe, release, and be in the moment. And sometimes, such as when using this journal, the bench may be a chair, a sofa, a bed, or even a floor. It is wherever you find it. Taking a moment to sit, pause, and reflect.

I often times sit on a bench and find inspiration for content for my daily 'practical inspiration' posting on Facebook. Along with my postings I try to provide a question of the day that hopefully allows you to pause for a moment in your full day and reflect.

A question I often share is: "How are you living your best self?" I sit with this question a lot and here is my humble offering....

Every day, I can't wait to get up and be in my day because I know that I'm going to come into contact with amazing people - from individual clients, to meeting people in places I frequent, to friends, family, community, and to classes I get to teach, etc. With each encounter there is always something to learn (thank you!) and to share (hopefully!) - from the smallest gesture of a smile to a long in-depth conversation.

I have yet to find the words to adequately express the joyful and inspirational feelings I get being in the presence of people sharing their gifts with the world. May we each continue to shine brightly for each other and for our self. We don't travel life's road alone.

Here's to each awesome moment, day, month, year ahead filled with unfolding possibilities. Who will you inspire? "Yes YOU Can!"

"Mindfulness is a pause. It's the space between reaction and response. That's where choice lives." – *Kerry McClure*

A FEW THOUGHTS ON GRATITUDE

Anytime is a perfect time to think about gratitude. It surrounds us. Unfortunately, we often find ourselves so busy in the course of living our lives that we forget to stop and take a moment to reflect on what we are grateful for. Or, if we do take a moment, it's a fleeting one. A whisper that touches our heart and then it's gone as we move back into the everyday moments that surround us. Much of our gratitude, once acknowledged, may not stick with us. We remember, of course, those exceptional moments, or those people who, for one reason or another, touch us deeply. But in moving through our lives these thoughts somehow find themselves as a sort of confetti in the background of a full life. Writing down these precious snippets, then, becomes the best way to remember them. To keep them in a way that prevents them from fading quite so easily into the background.

When Kerry and I talked about creating this journal one of the things that delighted us was the ability to pull together some of our favorite quotes. Also to put together pages that provided maximum flexibility. We both keep and give gratitude journals to others on a regular basis. The opportunity to create one is a joy.

I delight in having a place to write these heartfelt moments down because otherwise I find there are quite a number of things that escape me. In spite of my best efforts, if it's not written down it gets forgotten about. By having a journal I am grateful for those moments again. And I can revisit them anytime I want. I often go back, especially when I'm struggling with things that seem overwhelming, or there are challenges facing me. To go back into those moments reminds me that there are a lot of good things surrounding me.

However, many journals specifically designed to be gratitude journals seem to not have exactly what I'm looking for. They either have lines that say "I am grateful for _____" and you're expected to fill in the blanks (and only write enough for that one line). Maybe it's a journal that only has room for three gratitude comments per day but you have five things to share. Or it's simply a plain journal that is focused on gratitude because that's the purpose you've assigned to it. What we really wanted was to create something that had more flexibility and yet also provided inspiring quotes, scattered throughout, to help you focus on your moments of gratitude.

I specifically wanted blank pages that allowed me to doodle or write, free-flowing, as I chose. If you've read our previous book, *Beyond Meditation: making mindfulness accessible for everyone,* you'll know that's my favorite form of meditation. You may be surprised to know it's also a way that I use to practice gratitude. I write down a word or two that I'm grateful for in the middle of the page. And then I doodle around it, focusing on what I've written and allowing thoughts of gratitude for that moment, person, thing, to be upper most in my mind and heart. By having both blank and lined pages we're giving you the opportunity to use this journal any way you want. Write, doodle, draw, add stickers, paste articles, anything.

It's important to note that being grateful doesn't always come easy. When things are going well we are on top of the world and we think we've got it all right where we want it. We may not acknowledge the gratitude around us. And, when life is not so easy we may find ourselves feeling down in the dumps and overwhelmed. Often we get so overwhelmed that we allow the negative things to strongly influence how we perceive what is happening around us. And in the middle of the explosions of stress, worry, and overwhelming circumstance, the little sparks of gratitude can sometimes get lost. So just as we learn to read and write and do any of the other things we've learned to do in life, so too we need to learn to cultivate the habit of gratitude. Having a journal such as this one, where you can keep these moments together, helps you create that habit.

We're not here to tell you that if you journal gratitude every day you'll eventually come to live in that blissed out place that many imagine is a result of continual gratitude. I know I don't. I sometimes struggle to get there, to get anywhere close to being grateful for certain situations and circumstances. And yet I know I have so very much to be grateful for.

Yes we can get overwhelmed, sometimes we get lost. But both Kerry and I have come to believe that by remembering that concept of gratitude and by paying attention to it, we are happier overall. By cultivating that habit of remembering gratitude we learn to shift back into that mode even in the middle of challenging moments.

However you choose to use this journal, we hope you find inspiration in these pages, both from our humble offerings, as well as from those moments you will share in it's pages. *– Mira Dessy*

Move to your heart, Breathe. Close your eyes and breathe deeply - slowly - fill your lungs with love and gratitude - exhale each and every trouble - again and again - gratitude in, troubles out.

– JONATHAN LOCKWOOD HUIE

*I believe that meeting myself and others where we are with grace,
compassion and love creates a life filled with gratitude and abundance.*

– KERRY MCCLURE

No act of gratitude, no matter how small, is ever wasted.

– AESOP

Piglet noticed that even though he had a Very Small Heart,
it could hold a rather large amount of Gratitude.

– A.A. MILNE, WINNIE-THE-POOH

Gratitude makes sense of our past, brings peace for today and creates a vision for tomorrow.

– MELODY BEATTIE

*Showing gratitude is one of the simplest
yet most powerful things humans can do for each other.*

– RANDY PAUSCH

Let us be grateful to the people who make us happy;
they are the charming gardeners who make our souls blossom.

– MARCEL PROUST

*Cultivate the habit of being grateful for every good thing
that comes to you, and to give thanks continuously.*

— RALPH WALDO EMERSON

Be thankful for what you have; you'll end up having more.
If you concentrate on what you don't have, you will never, ever have enough.

– OPRAH WINFREY

Gratitude is not only the greatest of virtues, but the parent of all others.
– MARCUS TULLIUS

As we express our gratitude, we must never forget
that the highest appreciation is not to utter words, but to live by them.
– JOHN F. KENNEDY

Appreciate where you are at this moment
instead of always focusing on how far you have to go.

– MANDY HALE

Gratitude is the memory of the heart.

– JEAN BAPTISTE MASSIEU

There is a calmness to a life lived in gratitude, a quiet joy.

– RALPH H. BLUM

Wear gratitude like a cloak and it will feed every corner of your life.

– RUMI

Gratitude is the healthiest of all human emotions. The more you express gratitude for what you have, the more likely you will have even more to express gratitude for.

– ZIG ZIGLAR

When we give cheerfully and accept gratefully, everyone is blessed.

– MAYA ANGELOU

*When we express gratitude it lifts our vibrational frequency
and, by extension, can raise the frequency of those around us.*

– MIRA DESSY

Whatever we are waiting for — peace of mind, contentment, grace,
the inner awareness of simple abundance — it will surely come to us,
but only when we are ready to receive it with an open and grateful heart.

– SARAH BAN BREATHNACH

If the only prayer you ever say is "Thank You," that will be enough.

– ECKHART TOLLE

Gratitude is the single most important ingredient to living a successful and fulfilled life.

– JACK CANFIELD

*The miracle of gratitude is that it shifts your perception
to such an extent that it changes the world you see.*

– ROBERT HOLDEN

When you are grateful fear disappears and abundance appears.

– TONY ROBBINS

Begin each day with a grateful heart. Do what you can, wherever you are, with what you have to carry forth the message of compassion, kindness and gratitude into your day.

– KERRY MCCLURE

'Thank you' is the best prayer that anyone could say.
It expresses extreme gratitude, humility, understanding.

– ALICE WALKER

Be in a state of gratitude for everything that shows up in your life.
Be thankful for the storms as well as the smooth sailing.

– WAYNE DYER

Gratitude is when memory is stored in the heart and not in the mind.

– LIONEL HAMPTON

AUTHOR BIOGRAPHIES

KERRY MCCLURE is an author, speaker and wellness practitioner of nutrition, yoga, meditation, mindfulness, and fitness. She is co-author of the book *Beyond Meditation: making mindfulness accessible for everyone*, and creator of *"The Vibrant Life Method"* online wellness course. Kerry works with people to eat, move, and practice mindfulness for better energy; a clear, focused mind; and a long, healthy life. Kerry is passionate about helping her clients shift their lifestyle from "surviving" to "thriving" and from feeling "normal" to feeling "optimal". Kerry is board certified in Holistic Nutrition®. She's a member of the National Association of Nutrition Professionals and Yoga Alliance. She is certified in yoga, and several fitness modalities. She brings 25+ years of experience in corporate America to her company, Kerry McClure – Practical Wellness.

MIRA DESSY, THE INGREDIENT GURU, is an author, public speaker, and a Board Certified Holistic Health Practitioner who has been working with clients for over 10 years. She supports clients in reaching their health goals through holistic nutrition, lifestyle modifications, and chemical cleanup. She is the author of the book, *The Pantry Principle: how to read the label and understand what's really in your food* and the co-author of *Beyond Meditation: making mindfulness accessible for everyone*. A former meditation dropout, she's learned that just as with diets, there is no one-size-fits-all plan for everyone's mindfulness practice. Mira is on a mission to encourage others that if she can meditate so can you. She is a member of the National Association of Nutrition Professionals, the Society for Nutrition Education and Behavior, the American Association of Drugless Practitioners, the American Holistic Health Association, and is a founding member of the Health and Wellness Business Association.

OTHER TITLES

Beyond Meditation:
making mindfulness accessible for everyone

—···ᴄ ᴐ•0ᴐ 𝟿 ···—

AUTHOR CONTACT INFORMATION

MIRA DESSY *mira@theingredientguru.com*
www.TheIngredientGuru.com

KERRY MCCLURE *kerry@kerrymcclure.com*
www.kerrymcclure.com

Made in the USA
San Bernardino, CA
12 February 2018